TEACHERS

the
naked
truth

Knife & Packer

■SCHOLASTIC

Scholastic Children's Books,
Commonwealth House, 1-19 New Oxford Street,
London WC1A 1NU, UK

A division of Scholastic Ltd
London ~ New York ~ Toronto ~ Sydney ~ Auckland
Mexico City ~ New Delhi ~ Hong Kong

Published in the UK by Scholastic Ltd, 2001

Text and illustrations copyright © Knife & Packer, 2001

ISBN 0 439 99226 5

All rights reserved
Printed by Cox & Wyman Ltd, Reading, Berks

2 4 6 8 10 9 7 5 3 1

The right of Knife & Packer to be identified as authors and illustrators of this work
has been asserted by them in accordance with the Copyright, Designs and Patents
Act, 1988.

Contents

$2 \times 2 = 4$

ABC

**To our parents
(even though they sent us to school)**

1

WHERE DO TEACHERS COME FROM?

Teachers – everyone has them. There are fat ones, thin ones, hairy ones, bald ones... There's probably one somewhere with a head shaped like a sausage.

But let's face it, they all have one thing in common: *they're not like other people.* What's so different about them? Let's take a closer look at...

YOUR TEACHER!

GRUMPY FACE. FACT: WILL FRIGHTEN EVEN THE FLUFFIEST KITTEN

BAD HAIR. FACT: MOST TEACHERS HAVE 365 BAD HAIR DAYS A YEAR

BAGS UNDER EYES. FACT: AND THEY'RE BIG ENOUGH TO CARRY A WEEK'S SHOPPING

ELBOW PATCHES WHAT <u>ARE</u> THEY FOR?

POCKETS WHY DO THEY CARRY SO MANY DIFFERENT COLOURED PENS WHEN THEY ONLY EVER USE RED?

STAINED BLOUSE. FACT: YOU COULD LIVE ON THIS FOR A WEEK

HOMEWORK

SMELLY OLD TRAINERS: LIKE A CHEESE SHOP ON A HOT SUMMER'S DAY

HAIRY LEGS: ON SHOW TO FRIGHTEN SMALL DOGS

Yuk! But you don't just become a teacher overnight. Teachers don't come ready made do they? They don't just grow on trees...

HAVE YOU BEEN UP ALL NIGHT?

LEAF ME ALONE!

HOW'S IT HANGING, MISS ROBINSON?

Imagine if they did:

BLAH BLAH BLAH

your teacher might take root in the classroom!

So where *do* teachers come from?

The truth is that they're actually real, living, breathing people! If you don't believe us try this "SILLY DAFT EXPERIMENT" and find out for yourself. Give your teacher a tickle!

So why would a normal person want to become a teacher? Is it because they've tried other jobs and it's been a complete disaster? Imagine *your* teacher trying any of these...

Or maybe it's because of the "Job Genie"? Legend has it that a mysterious Job Genie decides what you'll become at birth…

Like all legends this should be taken with a pinch of salt (in fact make that a ton). All right we confess! We invented the Job Genie! It's just that the NAKED TRUTH is almost *too* awful to reveal…

Teachers don't come from anywhere special, some people actually decide that they want to become teachers. It could happen to one of your friends! So keep an eye out for any of these tell-tale signs:

2

TEACHING - THE BARE FACTS

Every day your teacher stands up at the front of the class and you have to put up with this:

blah blah bla
blah blah blah
blah blah blah
blah blah blah

They go on and on while you have to listen ... it's called teaching. But you may be surprised to hear that to be this boring takes a lot of work.

13

Teachers don't just turn up and talk about the first thing that comes into their head. They actually have to prepare. Yes, even teachers get homework! Let's sneak a look...

So while you're out playing with friends after school ... spare a thought for your teacher (that must have taken 1.3 nanoseconds!).

There are *plenty* of things your teacher would rather be doing. . .

Having prepared the class it's time to teach! It might surprise you to learn that we've identified over 200,000 different ways to teach. Do any of these seem familiar?

Unfortunately, we couldn't fit the other 199,994 ways of teaching on the one page.

Every sort of teacher is annoyed by something different.

One thing *every* teacher dreams of is the perfect class.
And we can now reveal to you exactly what that class
looks like...

And before you start to think you've got the upper hand, here's an **URGENT WARNING**. Deep in a bunker at a top-secret location, a crack team of teachers is already putting the final touches to the teacher of the future...

This technological wonder will be the scourge of all classrooms in the 21st Century! Hold onto your pencil cases as we bring you...

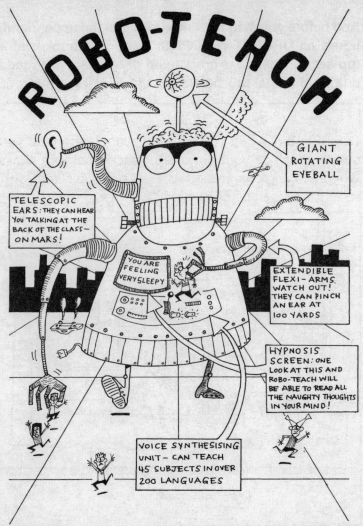

ROBO-TEACH

GIANT ROTATING EYEBALL

TELESCOPIC EARS: THEY CAN HEAR YOU TALKING AT THE BACK OF THE CLASS— ON MARS!

YOU ARE FEELING VERY SLEEPY

EXTENDIBLE FLEXI-ARMS. WATCH OUT! THEY CAN PINCH AN EAR AT 100 YARDS

HYPNOSIS SCREEN: ONE LOOK AT THIS AND ROBO-TEACH WILL BE ABLE TO READ ALL THE NAUGHTY THOUGHTS IN YOUR MIND!

VOICE SYNTHESISING UNIT – CAN TEACH 45 SUBJECTS IN OVER 200 LANGUAGES

Twenty-four hours a day, 365 days of the year (only stopping for the occasional recharge) Robo-teach never stops teaching. **LESSONS WILL NEVER BE THE SAME AGAIN!**

3

THE CLASSROOM UNCOVERED

Day after day when you come to school where do you spend most of your time? In your classroom that's where ... hang on a second did we say YOUR classroom? It's not YOUR classroom at all is it?

No, it's your TEACHER'S classroom, in fact we can reveal the NAKED TRUTH, that to your teacher, your classroom is in fact their personal...

22

The only trouble with their Kingdom is that as long as you're there, teachers have to be on their guard in case of a revolution. So, although to you the classroom looks like this...

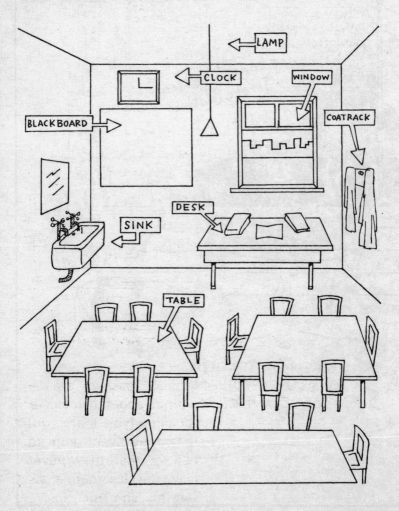

24

To your teacher it looks more like this...

LAMP = TRAPEZE

SINK = BREEDING PLACE FOR NASTY AQUATIC LIFE

WINDOW = ESCAPE HATCH

you've got the rest of the day off

DESK = BED

ZZZZ

COATRACK: HIDING PLACE FOR NAUGHTY PUPILS

TABLE: UPTURNED IT BECOMES A GREAT ESCAPE RAFT

In fact, teachers are so worried about their slaves rebelling (yes, that's you) that they want you to believe that they never leave the classroom at all. **But this isn't true**.

FOR THE FIRST TIME EVER, WE CAN EXPOSE THE SECRET PASSAGEWAYS THAT TEACHERS USE TO GET FROM THEIR HOMES TO THE CLASSROOM...

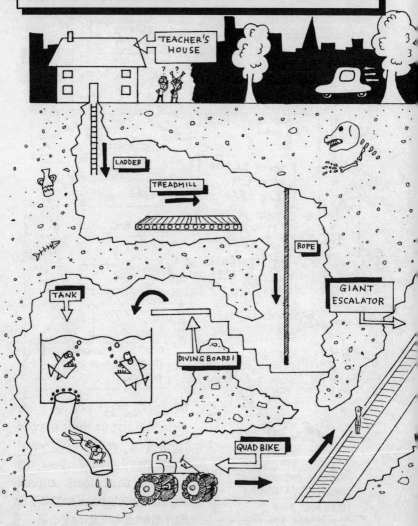

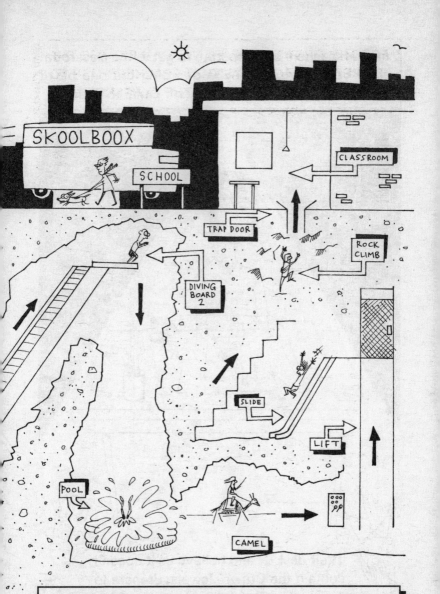

... AND THAT EXPLAINS WHY THEY'RE ALWAYS AT THE FRONT OF THE CLASS WHEN YOU COME IN!

Why are teachers so desperate to get to the classroom before you? Simple. They're guarding the one bit of the classroom that's completely off limits to you...

Their desk ... and believe us it doesn't contain the Crown Jewels. Prepare to be shocked as we take a peek inside!

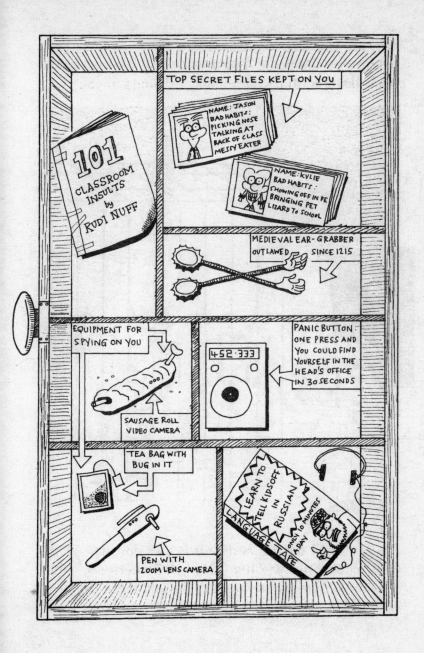

So now you know why teachers are so keen to keep you out! And why, for most teachers, *this* would be the ideal classroom...

You couldn't get up to much trouble in here, could you? Now you know the NAKED TRUTH about "your" classroom. So beware if your teacher starts taking an unhealthy interest in metalwork!

4

WHAT LURKS BEHIND THE STAFFROOM DOOR?

There is one place even more important to the teacher than their classroom, even more secret than their desk...yes, you can probably tell by the title of this chapter it's ... the STAFFROOM!

What's so great about the staffroom? Why do teachers rush there at every possible opportunity? What lurks behind that door? Is it...

SOME SORT OF PARADISE?

Come on, it's where teachers want to spend their free time so it's nothing like this. The NAKED TRUTH about the staffroom is, it's really, really...

34

And the things teachers get up to in the staffroom are of course frighteningly...

Boring...

So if you ever thought you wanted to go in for a look, don't bother, it just isn't worth the trouble – and you could well die of boredom.

But the NAKED TRUTH about teachers is: what *you* find tragically boring *they* find fantastically exciting.

Which explains why they look so depressed when they leave the staffroom and have to come back to the challenge and excitement of teaching YOU.

5

SCHOOL DINNERS – A SECRET WEAPON?

The bell goes and it's the most dreaded time of the day
... **IT'S DINNER TIME!** But cheer up, because there is
one good thing about school dinners: your teacher has
to eat them too!

And did you know that there is only
one place in the school where your
teacher isn't the boss?

So why is it that dinner ladies aren't scared of teachers? We can let you in on a little secret, it's because they've all done time here:

And now, for the first time ever, we're about to spill the beans on a place even your teacher hasn't dared go, as we reveal what goes on behind that kitchen door. *(Grab onto a bucket, you could be in for a queasy ride.)*

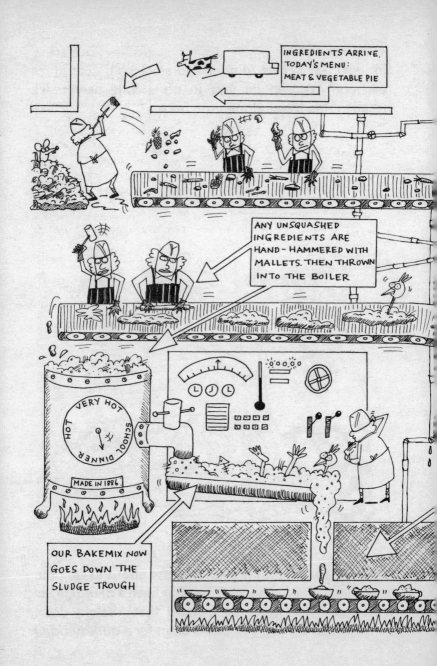

42

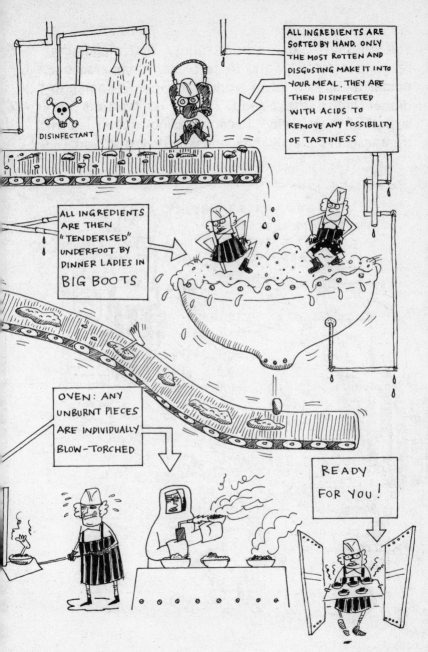

ALL INGREDIENTS ARE SORTED BY HAND. ONLY THE MOST ROTTEN AND DISGUSTING MAKE IT INTO YOUR MEAL. THEY ARE THEN DISINFECTED WITH ACIDS TO REMOVE ANY POSSIBILITY OF TASTINESS

DISINFECTANT

ALL INGREDIENTS ARE THEN "TENDERISED" UNDERFOOT BY DINNER LADIES IN BIG BOOTS

OVEN: ANY UNBURNT PIECES ARE INDIVIDUALLY BLOW-TORCHED

READY FOR YOU!

43

Yes, to make your school dinner *that* disgusting requires a lot of work. In fact, *eating* your school dinner requires a lot of work. And when it comes to dinner ladies the NAKED TRUTH is: teachers are scared of them! Why? Because school dinner ladies treat teachers exactly the same way they treat you.

At last we've discovered something you have in common with your teachers ... you don't like school dinners. So what could you do with all that food? Here's another "SILLY DAFT EXPERIMENT" you can do. Why not discover the alternative uses for school dinners and build a house out of them?

PIES USED AS BRICKS

ICE-CREAM WAFERS FOR ROOF-TILES

CUSTARD USED AS CONCRETE

MASHED POTATO USED TO HOLD IN WINDOW FRAMES

PEAS FOR GRAVEL ON THE DRIVE

JELLY USED FOR WINDOWS

OF COURSE, YOU WOULDN'T WANT ANYONE TO LIVE IN A HOUSE LIKE THIS, WOULD YOU?

YEEECH

EXCEPT, PERHAPS, A TEACHER?

6

THE PLAYGROUND - YIPEE!

OK, your teacher rules the classroom, but when it comes to the playground, who's in charge? Yes, teachers might have a whistle to blow, but this time *you're* the one who's having all the fun.

And this has always been the case. **Time for a history lesson…**

In the beginning there was a school,

and in that school there were some children...

and when the school bell sounded for break time...

DONG

they would run to the playground

and be naughty...

From the beginning of time the problem has been the same: *how do teachers stop pupils from getting into trouble?*

1. In the old days they tried the lifeguard seat.

2. More recently teachers have turned to new technology, using surveillance cameras.

3. And one day soon they'll be able to watch you from outer space.

Yes, teachers reckon you've had your own way for far too long. And in a staffroom near you they are plotting their perfect playground...

And it would look like this...

So enjoy your playground while you still can! And don't forget: *the more fun you're having the less fun your teacher's having*!

YOU

YOUR TEACHER

1 HAPPY = 1A GRUMPY

2 VERY HAPPY = 2A VERY GRUMPY

3 SUPER HAPPY = 3A SUPER GRUMPY

4 SUPER-DUPER EXTRA HAPPY (with sprinkles on top) = 4A LET'S NOT EVEN GO THERE!

7

REVENGE OF THE TEACHERS

There are certain things that should **NEVER** go together:

" SPINACH
&
ICE CREAM "

" GERBILS
&
TIGERS

" HAIR
&
CUSTARD "

But these are **NOTHING** compared to...

Yes, open evenings: these are the dreaded nights when parents and teachers get together to talk about you. **SCARY**!!!

Your teachers finally get to spill the beans about *you*! They tell your mum and dad *every little thing* you've done (and perhaps even a few that you haven't).

Yes – **YOU** are in the spotlight, **YOU** are centre stage. **YOU** are front page news! Just turn the page…

Daily Mail

PRICE: FREE FROM YOUR TEACHER

WHO'S THE HUNKIEST HEAD?

FIND OUT ON P.9

EXCLUSIVE

DISGRACE

BY OUR SPECIAL CORRESPONDENTS: ANNE GREE-TEACHER, ANNE NOYD-PARENT and FRANK LEE-TERRIBLE

EXPOSED

PARENTS WERE SHOCKED TO LEARN YESTERDAY THAT THEIR KIDS HAD DONE VERY BADLY AT SCHOOL.

REVEALED

THERE HAS BEEN FREQUENT TALKING AT THE BACK OF THE CLASS, ON THE SCHOOL BUS AND AT THE POOL.

444 3201

444 3201

MY BAD REPORT HELL

By Hope LESS

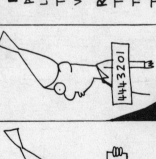

MISS JOHNSON RECEIVING THE MAGNIFICENT "BEAN-SPILLER OF THE YEAR" AWARD FROM THE LORD MAYOR.

UNCOVERED

AN INCIDENT INVOLVING THE BLOWING OF A RASPBERRY DURING P.E. LED TO A SENDING OUT.

CHAINSAW

FORTUNATELY NO CHAINSAWS WERE INVOLVED (THIS TIME).

SEE PAGES 23 - 37

OCTOPUS

THERE HAS BEEN A BLANKET BAN ON ALL SCHOOL FIELD TRIPS TO THE AQUARIUM FOLLOWING AN INCIDENT INVOLVING AN OCTOPUS, THREE SQUID AND A SHRIMP.

Egg and Spoon Race 2 p.m.

SPORTS NEWS

AN INCIDENT AT SCHOOL SPORTS DAY HAS LEFT EVERYONE WITH EGG ON THEIR FACE. READ MEG YOLK'S FULL REPORT IN OUR SIZZLING SPORTS PAGES.

Unfortunately for you, open evenings are a fact of life. But if you've worked hard you've nothing to fear. If you haven't then don't bother trying any of these...

(They just don't work – and we should know, we've tried them all.)

TEACHER'S TORMENT: FIELDTRIPS

Only a fieldtrip could turn a dusty old museum (where even the octopus is asleep)...

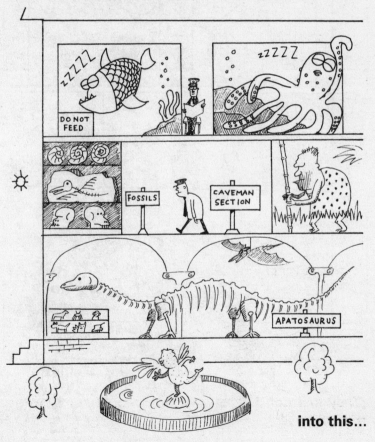

into this...

62

Yes, what could be more fun?

Unfortunately your teacher does have to come along...

But that's good! Teachers *hate* fieldtrips. Why? Because no matter where they go, the outcome is *always* the same...

They'd much rather be somewhere boring – without you! And when we say boring we mean *really* boring...

So boring we advise you to check you're sitting down before turning the page – it's the fieldtrip every teacher can't wait to go on – IT'S...

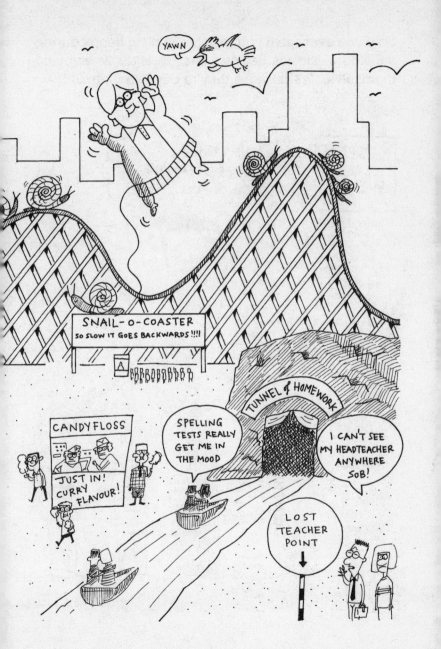

67

So if you ever catch your teacher looking happy during a fieldtrip it's not because they're actually enjoying themselves, it's because they're daydreaming...

9

SPORT - SPOILT

Does this look familiar?

Sports lessons – where *you* get to sweat buckets and your *teachers* don't.

In fact teachers and sport don't really mix, do they? Can you imagine your teacher doing any of these?

Ridiculous! The NAKED TRUTH is that most teachers' idea of sport is this...

THE TEACHER WORKOUT

5 EASY STEPS TO BECOMING A FITTER, HEALTHIER, HAPPIER TEACHER

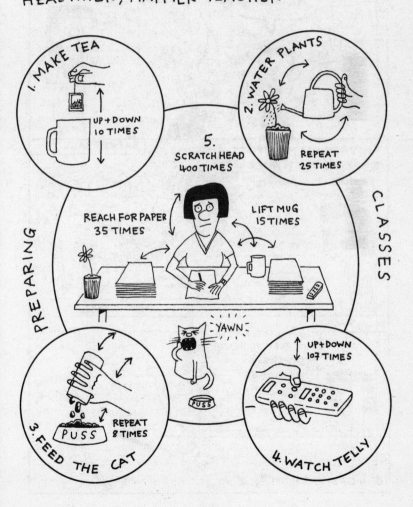

1. MAKE TEA — UP + DOWN 10 TIMES

2. WATER PLANTS — REPEAT 25 TIMES

5. SCRATCH HEAD 400 TIMES

REACH FOR PAPER 35 TIMES

LIFT MUG 15 TIMES

PREPARING

CLASSES

YAWN

3. FEED THE CAT — REPEAT 8 TIMES — PUSS

4. WATCH TELLY — UP + DOWN 107 TIMES

And when you're doing sport we can reveal what your teacher is *really* thinking...

While you huff and puff they're quite happy to stand around watching. But at the swimming pool on a hot summer's day it's a different story...

Let's be fair to the teachers for once. It's time *they* got in the pool.

Fair to teachers? You must be joking! Not in this book! That's why we chucked in some wildlife to make it more interesting.

And finally – school sports day – there's nothing like a day in the sunshine, everyone running, jumping and throwing things...

And unfortunately most school sports days are *nothing* like a day in the sunshine. In fact they're more like this...

Aliens, dinosaurs, volcanoes? OK, so we went to a pretty rough school. But there's no denying most sports days usually end in disaster!

10

HOMEWORK - THE HORROR, THE HORROR

You've been at school all day, you get back tired and exhausted. What do you do?

Oh sorry, you don't actually have a choice, do you? You've got HOMEWORK to do. That little bit of school you get to take home with you ... and the worst part about it is...

The pleasure it gives your teacher! The *worse* it is for you, the *better* it is for them.

They love everything about it...

But, if they were given the chance, your homework would be more like this:

You might find this hard to believe, but there is one good thing about homework...

When we said teachers love EVERYTHING about homework, we forgot to say that teachers HATE marking it! And yes, even teachers find reading your homework boring. Some of them even try to make it a little bit more interesting for themselves by...

So, no matter how much you hate homework, remember the NAKED TRUTH: you only have your own homework to do, but your teacher has to mark the work of *everyone* in your class!

11

EXPOSED! WHAT TEACHERS DO OUTSIDE SCHOOL!

When was the last time you bumped into a teacher outside school? Doesn't happen very often, does it? So where do they go to when they're not at school?
Is there a teacher keeper who locks them up at night?

Teacher keepers? It's not as silly as it sounds! **The NAKED TRUTH is much more sinister...**

Teachers live in homes just like yours! In fact, there could be a teacher living just round the corner from you...

Watch out for these telltale signs...

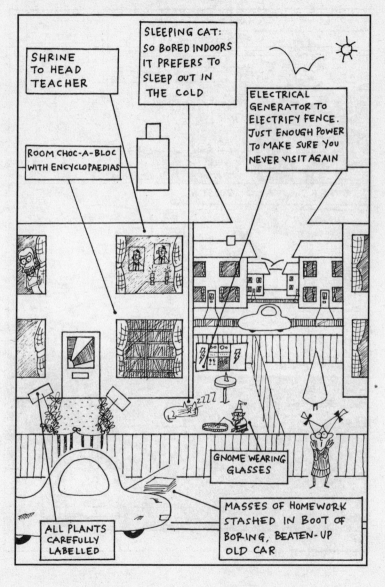

And this is why you don't see teachers more often.

But most of all ...

They don't hang out in the same places as you. You'll find that in their spare time they have *slightly* different hobbies from you.

Yes, teachers live in a different world. A world where *everyone* and *everything* needs a bit of teaching.

And what about holidays? This is you and your mates when the holidays start.

But can you spot the teacher in the background looking a bit sad? As a matter of fact, teachers *do* go on holiday...

But they're *still* in their own little world, and they *still* behave like teachers!

Of course, they have a really boring time on holiday, but that's just what teachers like! And you'll be pleased to hear that you're never very far from their thoughts...

So the NAKED TRUTH is that what teachers do after school (and even on holiday) is incredibly boring. If you're unlucky enough to spot one after school **take cover** – who knows, being boring might be contagious!

AND THAT'S THE NAKED TRUTH!

Let's face it, after reading this book you'll *never* be able to look at your teacher in the same way again.

94

And if you bought this book hoping to see a

you won't be *entirely* disappointed...